INTRODUCTION

◆

Scientists say the Universe was created about 13.8 billion years ago by the Big Bang. This happened when something thousands of times smaller than a grain of salt exploded and expanded at super speed. In a fraction of a second, the Universe was already bigger than a galaxy and as hot as billions of degrees centigrade. After about 300,000 years, it had cooled to around 3,000 °C and began to be filled with clouds of hydrogen and helium gas. Between 200 to 400 million years later, these gases had collapsed enough to form stars and galaxies. From gas and dust, the Sun began to form about 4.6 billion years after the Big Bang. Then, with the bits left over that made the Sun, the planets were created. Our planet, Earth, is thought to be approximately 4.5 billion years old.

Our solar system contains a star, the Sun, and the objects that orbit around it. These include the eight planets, dwarf planets like Pluto, moons and asteroids. This book will take you on a journey to explore these objects, plus many of the incredible inventions, such as rockets, rovers and satellites, which humans have created to explore our solar system. So press out the pages and have fun creating your very own work of art in a book.

→ GO TO PAGE 39
FOR THE GAS GIANTS

→ GO TO PAGE 37
FOR THE
PERSEVERANCE ROVER

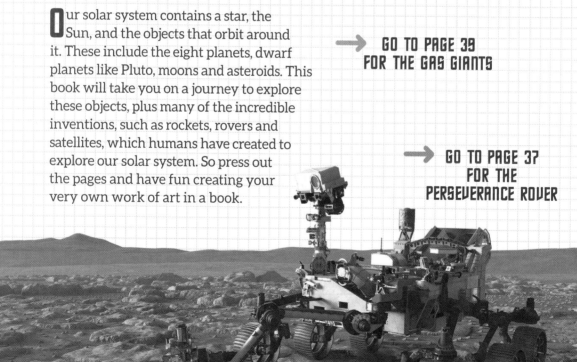

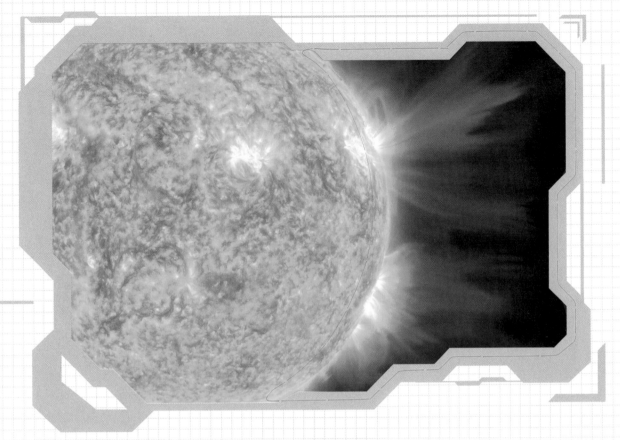

THE SUN

The Sun is Earth's closest star and the biggest object in our solar system. It is a giant ball of gas, made up of 92 per cent hydrogen and eight per cent helium. It is so huge that 1.3 million Earths could fit inside it! At its centre, which is also known as its core, the Sun is a mind-bogglingly hot 15 million °C. Its surface, which is also called its photosphere, is around 5,500 °C – but that's still hot enough to vaporise a diamond! The nuclear energy that the Sun produces at its core takes 170,000 years to reach the convective zone, which is next to the surface. The energy in this zone provides heat and light on Earth.

RADIUS (THE DISTANCE FROM ITS CENTRE TO ITS SURFACE):
695,700 km

- -

AVERAGE DISTANCE FROM EARTH:
149.6 million km

- -

FORMED:
about 4.5 billion years ago

- -

STAR TYPE:
yellow dwarf

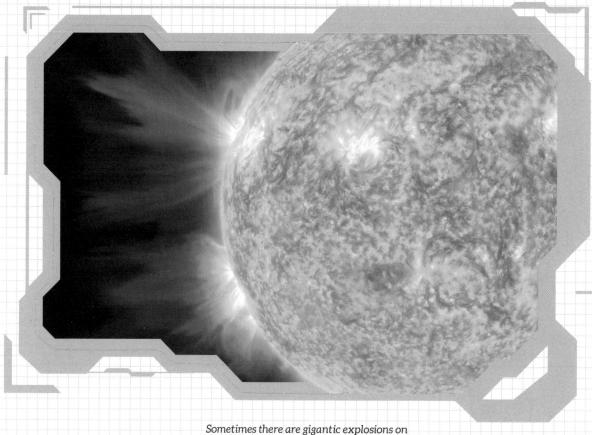

Sometimes there are gigantic explosions on the surface of the Sun, called flares.

DID YOU KNOW...?

❓ Sunlight takes around eight minutes to reach Earth from the Sun.

❓ The Sun has 99.8 per cent of the mass in the solar system. Mass is the amount of matter in an object. More matter means a bigger mass.

❓ About 11,760 Earths could fit in a line between the Earth and the Sun, which shows how far away that big yellow dot really is!

Besides the eight planets in the solar system, the Sun has plenty of other objects orbiting (travelling around) it, including at least five dwarf planets, thousands and thousands of asteroids, and trillions of comets and other small space objects. One day, the Sun will run out of energy, but don't worry – scientists reckon the Sun is only halfway through its life cycle and still has another 6.5 billion years to go! When it begins to die, scientists predict it will get bigger and bigger until it swallows up the closest three planets – Mercury, Venus and Earth. This process could take millions of years and means the Sun will turn into a red giant star. As a red giant, the Sun could be 2,000 times brighter than it is now.

THE ROCKY INNER PLANETS

Mercury, Venus, Earth and Mars are the four planets closest to the Sun, in that order. They were probably formed around 4.5 billion years ago from a cloud of dust and gas in space that collapsed. They are all made up of a core in the centre, surrounded by a mantle of rocks and a solid crust under the surface. These four planets are called the inner planets because they orbit inside the asteroid belt surrounding the Sun. Earth is the only planet we know that can support life. Its atmosphere (the gases that surround it) is breathable, it has liquid water and the right level of heat and light from the Sun.

MERCURY
RADIUS*: 2,439.7 km **ADFS***: 58 million km

VENUS
RADIUS: 6,052 km **ADFS**: 108 million km

EARTH
RADIUS: 6,371 km **ADFS**: 150 million km

MARS
RADIUS: 3,390 km **ADFS**: 228 million km

*all radii are averages *average distance from the Sun

NASA describes Earth's mantle, which is between
the outer core and crust, as a molten rock layer that
has a texture a bit like caramel!

DID YOU KNOW...?

❓ All of the planets, except for Earth, are named after Roman or Greek goddesses or gods. Venus is the Roman goddess of love.

❓ Scientists think an asteroid hit Earth about 65 million years ago, causing the extinction of many animals, including the dinosaurs.

❓ Two robotic spacecraft have come close to Mercury: Mariner 10 flew by in 1974 and Messenger orbited between 2011 and 2015.

Mars is extremely cold and dusty but scientists still get very excited about this red planet. In fact, Mars is the most explored planet in our solar system. The reason for this is that it shares lots of similarities with Earth. Like Earth, Mars has weather that changes with its seasons, and it even has ice caps at its north and south poles. Scientists think Mars was probably warmer and wetter billions of years ago and clues on its surface suggest it may even have had salt-water floods that flowed down its hills and craters. Because Mars might have contained water in the past, it may also have supported life. Both scientists and space fans hope that one day humans will be able to set foot on its surface.

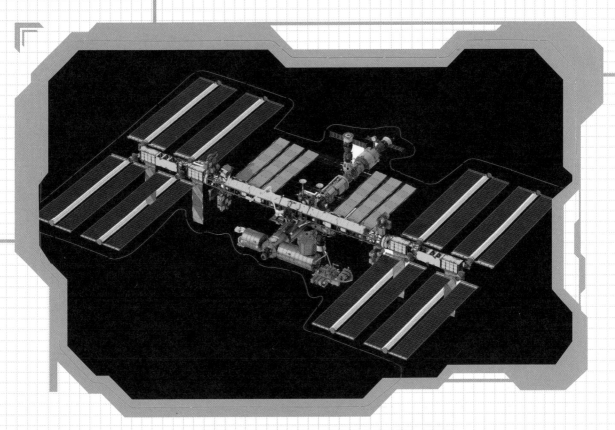

THE INTERNATIONAL SPACE STATION

It's the most amazing space machine ever created! Orbiting around 400 kilometres above the Earth at a speed of 28,200 kilometres an hour, the International Space Station (ISS) has been a permanent home for astronauts since 2000. Up to six astronauts and cosmonauts can live together on the ISS at one time and its main purpose is to conduct experiments in low Earth orbit. The ISS takes just 90 minutes to travel around Earth and makes 16 orbits every 24 hours. The giant structure can be seen in the night sky without a telescope and is the brightest object we can view in the sky after the Sun and Moon.

CREATED: between 1998 and 2011

LENGTH: 109 m

MASS: 419,725 kg

POWERED BY: 262,400 solar cells

ESTIMATED COST: over $100 billion

Each of the ISS's solar arrays is longer than a passenger plane and together they can produce enough power to run 40 homes!

Sometimes astronauts and cosmonauts have to work outside the ISS. Over 205 spacewalks have taken place.

DID YOU KNOW...?

? Over 230 astronauts and cosmonauts from 18 countries have flown to the ISS.

? There's only a tiny amount of gravity on the ISS, so astronauts exercise for two hours every day to stop their muscles weakening.

? Fifteen countries worked together to build the ISS, including the US, Russia, Canada, France and Japan.

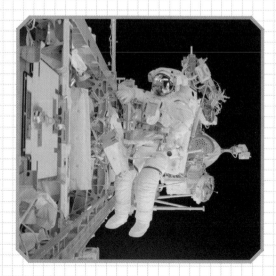

THE SPACE SHUTTLE

With its huge, orange, external fuel tank and twin solid rocket boosters, NASA's Space Shuttle blasting into the sky was a special sight during its 30-year life. In fact, six different Shuttles were made: Enterprise, Columbia, Challenger, Discovery, Endeavour and Atlantis. Their missions included carrying out space experiments and helping to build the International Space Station. NASA's incredible creation was the world's first reusable spacecraft. In total, the six Shuttles flew over 864 million kilometres, took 134 flights, made 20,952 orbits of Earth and carried 355 people into space.

OFFICIAL NAME:
Space Transportation System

- - - - - - - - - - - - - - - - - - -

ACTIVE: 1981–2011

- - - - - - - - - - - - - - - - - - -

TIME IN SPACE: 1,320 days

- - - - - - - - - - - - - - - - - - -

TOP SPEED: 28,164 km/h

- - - - - - - - - - - - - - - - - - -

TOTAL COST: $113.7 billion

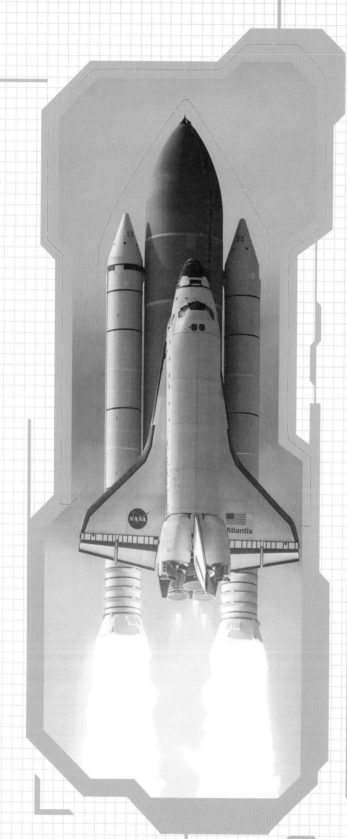

The Space Shuttle's huge orange section is its external tank (ET). The liquid oxygen and hydrogen inside powered its three main engines.

A special Boeing 747 Shuttle Aircraft Carrier transported the Space Shuttle between NASA sites. It looked very strange parked on top of the jumbo jet!

DID YOU KNOW...?

❓ John Glenn flew on the Space Shuttle Discovery in 1998. At 77 years old, he was the oldest person to travel in space.

❓ Space Shuttle Columbia had the longest single mission. It lasted 17 days, 15 hours, 53 minutes and 18 seconds.

❓ All of the Space Shuttles were around 56 metres long with a 24-metre wingspan and often carried a crew of seven astronauts.

ASTRONAUTS and COSMONAUTS

These highly trained human beings have one of the most exciting jobs on – and, of course, off – the planet! They travel on spacecraft and carry out missions such as going to the Moon and the International Space Station and they help take objects such as satellites into orbit. In Russia, astronauts are called cosmonauts. The first human in space was a Russian man called Yuri Gagarin in April 1961. Gagarin spent 108 minutes orbiting Earth in his Vostock 1 spacecraft. The first astronaut to land a spacecraft and then walk on the Moon was American Neil Armstrong in 1969.

Russian cosmonaut Valentina Tereshkova was the first woman to fly in space. In June 1963, aboard the Vostok 6 rocket, Tereshkova and her crew made 48 orbits of Earth.

Spacesuits are very expensive –
a new one could cost NASA
$250 million to build.

DID YOU KNOW...?

❓ In 2018, the European Space Agency (ESA) had eight active astronauts – seven male and one female.

❓ In 1965, Russia's Alexei Leonov performed the first spacewalk. He was outside his Voshod 2 spacecraft for 12 minutes.

❓ While on the ISS, British astronaut Tim Peake ran 42.2 kilometres (that's the same as a marathon) in three hours and 35 minutes on a treadmill!

The special white spacesuits that astronauts wear protect them during spacewalks. Their backpack is called the Primary Life Support Subsystem. It provides oxygen and removes exhaled carbon dioxide, and it has a battery pack. The helmet must be strong enough to withstand small objects hitting the astronaut's head. The visor on the helmet of a spacesuit has a thin layer of gold on it to shield the astronaut's eyes from the Sun's rays. Each suit has 14 special layers, which provide temperature control and protective support. It can take an astronaut 45 minutes to put their suit on. After that, they need to spend an hour breathing pure oxygen to adapt to the low pressure inside the suit.

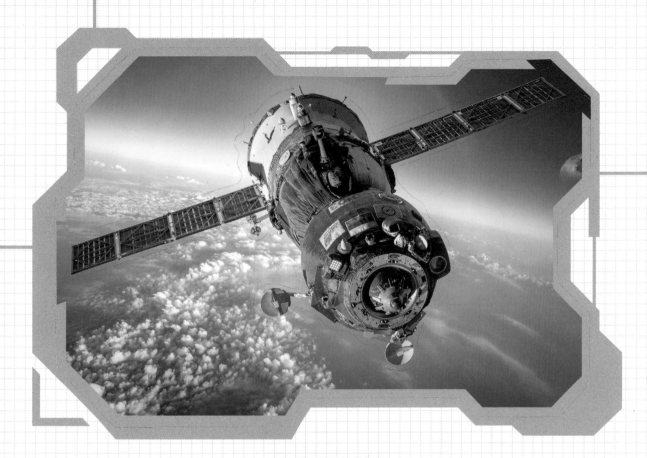

SOYUZ

Astronauts and cosmonauts reach the ISS by flying in the Soyuz (pronounced 'SAW-yooz') space capsule. Since NASA's Space Shuttle was retired in 2011, Soyuz has been the only spacecraft that takes humans and supplies to and from the ISS. Soyuz takes around six hours to fly a maximum of three astronauts or cosmonauts to the space station, but – thanks to gravity – it takes just three and a half hours to return! Placed at the top of the Soyuz rocket, the capsule reaches space in about nine minutes. Only the capsule docks (connects) with the ISS, allowing the crew to enter.

LENGTH OF CAPSULE: 7 m

WIDTH OF CAPSULE, EXCLUDING ARRAYS: 2.7 m

LAUNCHED FROM:
Baikonur Cosmodrome, Kazakhstan

LAUNCH ROCKET: Soyuz FG rocket

CREWED AND UNCREWED LAUNCHES: over 1,700

Each of the solar panels on Soyuz are 4.2 metres long – that's more than twice the length of a standard household door.

DID YOU KNOW...?

❓ Soyuz took its first crew to the ISS in November 2000. It launched from Russia, carrying two cosmonauts and one astronaut.

❓ When it lands on Earth, Soyuz uses small rocket engines and a parachute to slow to about 7.2 kilometres an hour.

❓ At least one Soyuz spacecraft is always docked at the ISS. It's the crew's emergency escape vehicle.

Design work on Soyuz began in 1960 and its first flight was in 1966. Its name means 'union' in Russian – which is apt as it's shared with the USA. It has completed more than 1,700 launches, making it the most successful launch vehicle ever. It has three modules. The orbital module is where astronauts and cosmonauts live while they are in orbit. It's about the size of a camper van. The descent module is used when Soyuz is launched or descends to Earth. It brings the crew back to Earth by dropping through the atmosphere and using its small rocket engines to land. The third module contains supplies such as batteries, solar panels and steering engines.

SKYLAB

NASA's first space station was called Skylab. It orbited Earth between 1973 and 1979, with the aim of developing experiments in space and proving humans could survive there for long periods. Skylab didn't always have astronauts on board. There were only three crewed missions to the space station, all in 1973. The longest mission was called Skylab III and three astronauts spent 84 days, one hour and 16 minutes away from Earth. Skylab was taken into space by the Saturn V rocket used in the Moon landings. Its three crews flew up to Skylab on the Saturn 1B rocket.

LENGTH: 35.6 m

MASS: 77,000 kg

DAYS IN ORBIT: 2,249

ASTRONAUTS ON BOARD FOR: 171 days

ESTIMATED COST: $2.2 billion

When NASA astronaut Charles Conrad performed a spacewalk on Skylab in 1973, he excitedly said, 'Every kid in the United States would have a blast up here!'

DID YOU KNOW...?

❓ The first ever space station was Russia's Salyut 1. It launched on 19 April 1971, and spent 175 days in orbit.

❓ In total, Skylab orbited Earth 34,981 times and travelled over 1.4 billion kilometres.

❓ NASA brought Skylab back to Earth in 1979. It broke up into small pieces that fell into the southeastern Indian Ocean and over parts of Western Australia.

Skylab's three three-person crews carried out an impressive 270 scientific and technical experiments on the space station. These tests tried to answer questions about biology, physics and astronomy and 90 different types of machinery were used to carry them out. The astronauts also made over 41 hours of spacewalks, called extravehicular activities, outside Skylab. One of the most famous experiments involved two common garden spiders, called Arabella and Anita. Astronauts studied the effects of microgravity and the spiders' ability to spin webs in space! One of the Skylab mission's most important achievements was doubling the length of time that humans had spent in space.

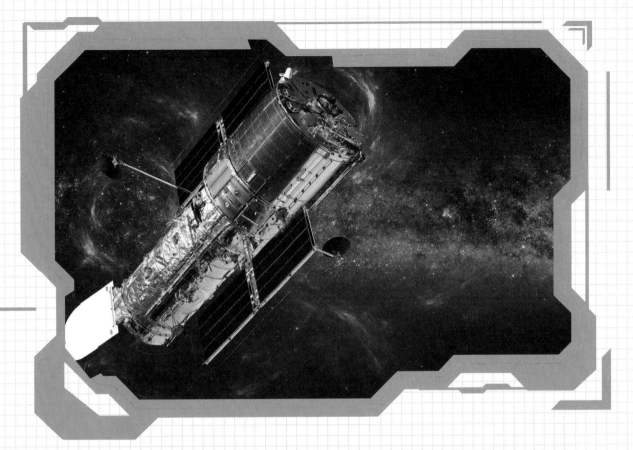

THE **HUBBLE SPACE TELESCOPE**

Orbiting in space about 547 kilometres above Earth, the Hubble Space Telescope has captured incredible images of galaxies, planets, the birth and death of stars, and much more. Blasted into space in 1990, it orbits Earth every 96 minutes and has made over 1.3 million observations. Its 2.4 metre-long primary mirror reflects light on to a smaller mirror and then the data is sent to Earth. Astronauts have repaired it five times in space – the last time was in 2009. Hubble can take such amazing images because it is away from the atmosphere, clouds and light pollution that affect telescopes on the ground.

LENGTH: 13.2 m

WIDTH: 4.2 m

MASS: 10,886 kg

SPEED: 27,300 km/h

DISTANCE TRAVELLED: over 6.4 billion km

*Hubble can focus on something
as thin as a human hair from
one kilometre away!*

*This amazing image taken by Hubble shows part
of one of the largest star-birth regions ever seen.
It's called the Carina Nebula.*

DID YOU KNOW...?

❓ Hubble's creation, launch and maintenance has cost around $10 billion.

❓ In 2018, Hubble spotted the most distant star ever seen. Called Icarus, its light takes nine billion years to reach Earth.

❓ Hubble is named after Edwin Hubble, an American astronomer who made important discoveries about stars and galaxies.

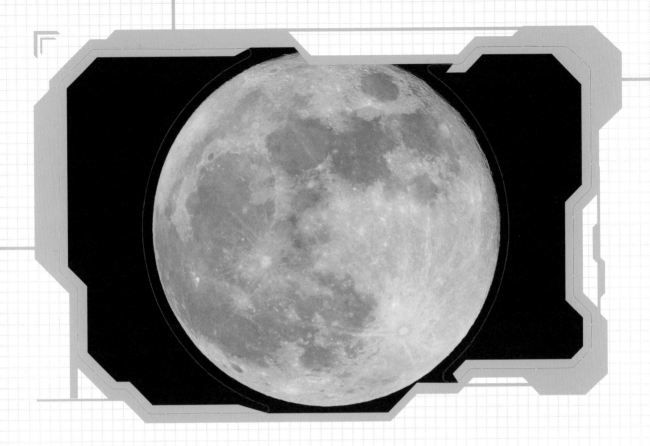

THE MOON

The Moon is incredible to study – and it's also easy to study because it's so close to Earth! It is thought to have been created about 4.5 billion years ago when an object about the size of Mars collided with Earth. The smashed pieces eventually came together to form the Moon, spinning in orbit around our planet. For around 100 million years, the Moon was hot and molten, and had active volcanoes, but then it began to cool and form a crust with magma bubbling underneath it. Slowly the magma formed into a thick mantle, surrounding an iron-rich core at the centre with a radius of 240 kilometres.

RADIUS: 1,737.5 km

AVERAGE TEMPERATURE: -173 °C–127 °C

AVERAGE DISTANCE FROM EARTH: 384,400 km

TIME TAKEN TO ORBIT EARTH: 27 days

GRAVITY: astronauts weigh six times less on the Moon – that's why they bounce along its surface, even in bulky spacesuits and boots

The lighter areas on the Moon's surface are called highlands and the darker areas show where lava once erupted.

The footprints left by the astronauts between 1969 and 1972 are still there today! The Moon has no wind to blow them away.

DID YOU KNOW...?

❓ You could fit 30 Earths in the distance between the Earth and the Moon, and it's travelling away from Earth at a speed of about 2.5 centimetres a year.

❓ The Moon doesn't create its own light – it reflects sunlight like the planets do.

❓ The Moon is only the fifth largest one in the solar system. Jupiter's Ganymede, Saturn's Titan and Jupiter's Callisto and Io are all bigger.

THE SATURN V ROCKET

Everything that goes into space needs a rocket to take it there. NASA's Saturn V (pronounced 'five') was the mega-powerful rocket that blasted the Apollo missions to the Moon in the 1960s and '70s. Twice the length of the Space Shuttle, the Saturn V's five F-1 rocket engines used 770,000 litres of kerosene fuel and 1.2 million litres of liquid oxygen to thrust it 68 kilometres above the launch pad. The Saturn V had three main stages (parts). Each stage burned its engines until its fuel ran out and then it would fall away. The Command Module that orbited the Moon and the Lunar Module that took astronauts to the Moon's surface were placed near the top.

HEIGHT: 111 m

LAUNCH WEIGHT: 2.8 million kg

ROCKET TYPE: Heavy Lift Vehicle

FIRST FLIGHT: 9 November 1967

LAST FLIGHT: 14 May 1973

PROJECT COST: $6.4 billion

The Saturn V rocket was about the height of a 36-storey building and was 18 metres taller than the Statue of Liberty in New York!

Before the Saturn V took astronauts to the Moon, two smaller Saturn rockets were built to carry humans into orbit around the Earth. Saturn I and Saturn IB proved that NASA's rocket system worked very well and that it had the potential to reach the surface of the Moon. A German rocket scientist called Dr Wernher von Braun was one of the most important people behind the success of the Saturn V. After developing rockets for Germany in World War II, he led the NASA team that built the Saturn V in the 1960s and helped achieve NASA's most celebrated mission of landing a human on the Moon.

DID YOU KNOW...?

? The pointed white top of the Saturn V is the launch escape system. It could drag the Command Module away from the Saturn V rocket in an emergency during launch.

? A car could drive around the world 800 times using the amount of fuel that the Saturn V carried.

? The final Saturn V launch didn't send astronauts to the Moon – it sent the Skylab space station into orbit.

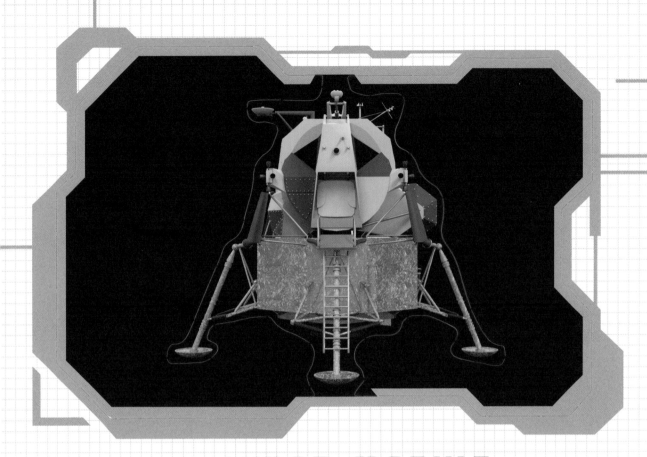

THE **LUNAR MODULE**

All six Moon landings were achieved by the American space agency, NASA, and they happened between 1969 and 1972. No human has been to the Moon since and the missions were part of the famous Apollo program. Apollo 11 launched from Cape Kennedy, Florida, on 16 July 1969, powered by a Saturn V rocket. Astronauts Neil Armstrong, Michael Collins and Buzz Aldrin were on board. Armstrong and Aldrin were inside Apollo 11's Lunar Module (LM), called Eagle, which separated from the bigger Command Module, Colombia, and touched down on the Moon's surface on 20 July.

HEIGHT: 6.9 m

DIAMETER: 7 m

MASS: 4,898 kg

FIRST LUNAR MODULE MOON LANDING:
20 July 1969 at 4:18pm (Eastern Daylight Time)

ESTIMATED COST OF LUNAR MODULES:
over $2.2 billion

*It's estimated that 530 million people watched on TV
as the Lunar Module landed on the Moon.*

DID YOU KNOW...?

❓ During the six Apollo Moon landings, astronauts collected 382 kilograms of rock, sand and dust samples to bring back to Earth.

❓ The Lunar Module had two parts: the ascent stage, that carried the crew, and descent stage, that landed it on the Moon.

❓ Armstrong stepped onto the Moon four days, 13 hours and 42 minutes after Apollo 11 launched from Earth.

Neil Armstrong was the first to step from the Lunar Module onto the Moon, followed by Buzz Aldrin. The two men ventured about 90 metres from their spacecraft to explore the Moon's surface, carried out experiments and collected samples. They spent 21 hours and 36 minutes on the Moon before returning to the Lunar Module and docking again with the Command Module. Ronald Evans, who was the Command Module pilot on Apollo 17, holds the record for the longest time spent in lunar orbit: six Earth days, three hours and 48 minutes. Only 12 astronauts have ever entered the Lunar Module and touched down on the Moon's bleak and dusty surface and only 24 humans have ever orbited the Moon.

LUNAR ROVING VEHICLES

Some of the most awesome high-tech kit ever used on the Moon by an astronaut was the Lunar Roving Vehicle (LRV). Nicknamed Moon buggies, three identical LRVs were used on three missions between 1971 and 1972. Their purpose was to help astronauts explore the Moon's surface further and undertake more experiments. These battery-powered machines had no steering wheel or pedal brakes and were controlled by a handle between the two seats. There was little danger of any high-speed crashes happening as they did an average speed of just eight kilometres an hour!

MISSIONS: Apollo 15, Apollo 16, Apollo 17

FRAME SIZE: 3.1 m long, 2.3 m wide, 1.14 m high

MASS: 210 kg

TOP SPEED: 18 km/h

MADE FROM: mostly aluminium alloy

Both sets of the LRV's wheels could turn in opposite directions to help with steering.

DID YOU KNOW...?

❓ The LRVs cost about $38 million, which probably makes them the most expensive four-wheeled machines ever made!

❓ The three LRVs were all left behind on the Moon when the astronauts left. A fourth was built and used for spare parts during their development on Earth.

❓ The LRV that astronauts trained in on Earth is on display at the Space Center, Houston, USA.

The Lunar Roving Vehicle was designed and built in just 17 months by NASA and the three LRVs sent to the Moon operated very well there. They were driven for a total of 10 hours and 54 minutes and in that time they covered 90.4 kilometres. The furthest any of the machines travelled from the Landing Module was 7.6 kilometres. Space fans back on Earth got to see live pictures of the LRVs exploring the Moon thanks to the LRVs' onboard TV cameras. Astronauts David Scott, Jim Irwin, John Young, Charles Duke, Gene Cernan and Harrison Schmitt were the lucky men who got to drive them! Each LRV had four-wheel drive, seatbelts, adjustable footrests and a dust guard behind each wheel.

THE SPACE LAUNCH SYSTEM

When NASA unleashes its Space Launch System it will be the most powerful rocket launcher on the planet! The SLS will be able to carry up to four astronauts into space. It could launch exciting robotic science missions to Mars, Saturn and Jupiter. The first version of the rocket, called Block 1, has more power than 160,000 Corvette sports cars. It is 98 metres tall, which is bigger than the Statue of Liberty, and it is hoped it will be able to carry about 95,000 kilograms of cargo and passengers – around four times what the Space Shuttle could carry.

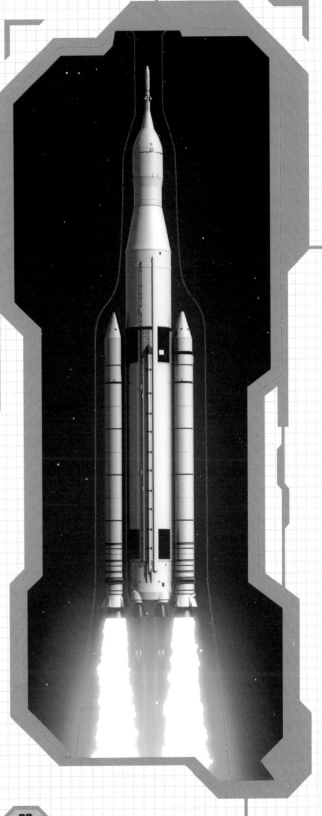

LENGTH: 98 m

- -

WIDTH: 8.3 m

- -

LAUNCH WEIGHT: 2.49 million kg

- -

ENGINES: Four S-25 rocket engines, two solid rocket boosters

- -

MAXIMUM PAYLOAD: 95, 000 kg

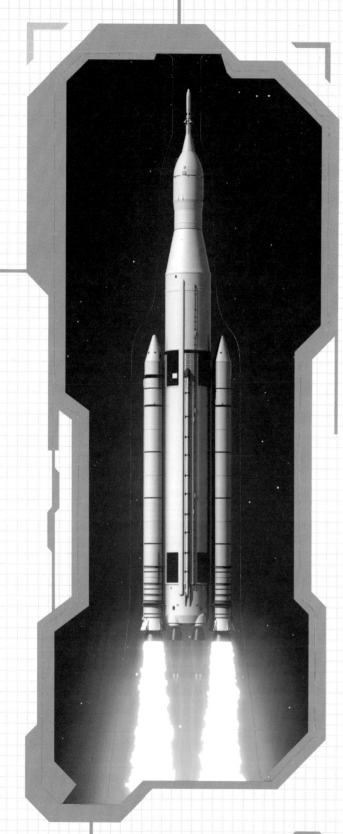

The Orion spacecraft will detach from the top of the SLS and take astronauts into orbit, or to the ISS, the Moon or Mars.

DID YOU KNOW...?

❓ The SLS has been designed to help carry out robotic missions to study the Moon, Mars, Saturn and Jupiter.

❓ The SLS will act as back-up transportation for taking astronauts to the International Space Station.

❓ During its three-week test flight, the SLS will travel more than 450,000 kilometres away from Earth.

SPACEX

Government-funded organisations aren't the only groups of people that send things into space – private companies are also working on space exploration. SpaceX was set up in 2002 by South African engineer and billionaire Elon Musk. So far it has designed, built and launched two huge rockets – Falcon 9 and Falcon Heavy – and a cargo-carrying spacecraft called Dragon. SpaceX rocketed to fame in 2018 when it sent an electric Tesla sports car into space. Connected to Falcon Heavy, the car had a dummy astronaut, called Starman, in the driver's seat and by May 2018 it was over 35 million kilometres from Earth.

SPACEX HEADQUARTERS: California

LAUNCH FACILITIES:
Kennedy Space Center, Florida
Vandenberg Air Force Base, California

EMPLOYEES: more than 5,000

ULTIMATE AIM: find ways to live on other planets

Researchers say there's a very small chance that SpaceX's Tesla car might crash into Earth – in the next million years!

The SpaceX Falcon Heavy is the most powerful rocket now in use. It can carry 64,000 kilograms into orbit and costs $90 million to launch.

DID YOU KNOW...?

❓ Elon Musk also owns the Tesla electric sports car company. The vehicle he launched into space was his own car!

❓ The Tesla that was launched into space is travelling away from Earth at a speed of around 12,000 kilometres an hour.

❓ SpaceX is working towards flying future missions to Mars as well as sending spacecraft into orbit around the Moon.

OPPORTUNITY ROVER

After landing on the surface of Mars in January 2004, the six-wheeled robotic rover Opportunity became a record breaker. It was the rover that covered the most distance on Mars – over 45 kilometres – before it ceased communicating with Earth. As part of the Mars Exploration Program, its goal was to search the planet's rocks and soil for signs of water activity in the past. Opportunity had many tools to help it explore the Martian landscape, including a robotic arm, a rock drill, several cameras, and a very special tool called a spectrometer that uses radioactive X-rays to study the surface in detail.

LAUNCHED: 7 July 2003

AVERAGE SPEED: 0.18 km/h

LENGTH: 2.3 m

HEIGHT: 1.5 m

DISTANCE COVERED: over 45 km

Opportunity carried cameras for three different purposes: navigation, avoiding hazards and collecting images for research purposes.

DID YOU KNOW...?

❓ Opportunity was launched by a Delta II heavy rocket and a landing craft carried it to the surface of Mars.

❓ Opportunity's mission was only meant to last 90 days – but it lasted nearly 15 years.

❓ Another Mars rover, Curiosity, touched down in 2012. Its mission: to find out if there had ever been life on Mars, to study its climate and surface, and to work out if the planet could support human life.

In 2015, NASA scientists celebrated Opportunity covering 42.195 kilometres on Mars – that's the same distance as a marathon! While some humans can run a marathon in just over two hours, it took Opportunity 11 Earth years and two Earth months to cover the distance, or 3,968 Martian days! The previous record for the longest distance covered by a non-Earth-based rover was Russia's Lunokhod 2. In 1973, it covered an impressive 37 kilometres across the surface of the Moon. An identical rover to Opportunity, called Spirit, also flew to Mars on the same mission. It stopped working after six years and covered 7.73 kilometres. During its mission, Spirit took over 124,000 images.

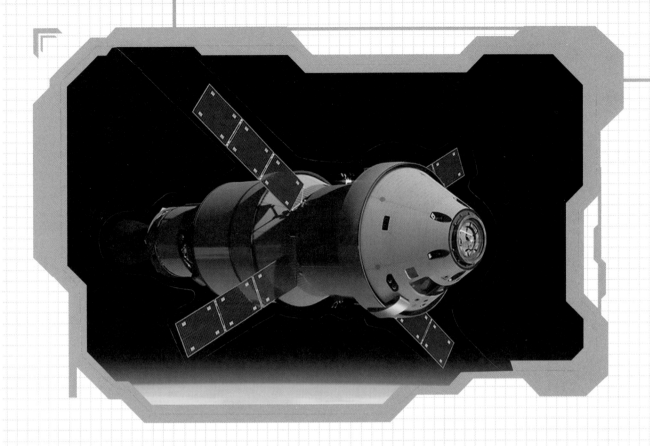

ORION SPACECRAFT

The Orion spacecraft will aim to take humans further into space than ever before! The futuristic machine is being built and tested by NASA. It will blast off with the help of the Space Launch System and could carry astronauts for months as they journey beyond the Moon. In the future, it could touch down on asteroids and even Mars. The part of the Orion spacecraft that houses the astronauts is called the crew module. Underneath the crew module is the service module, which carries water and oxygen, and separates from the crew module in orbit before it descends to Earth.

DIAMETER OF CREW MODULE: 5 m

LAUNCH WEIGHT: 10,387 kg (crew module)

NUMBER OF CREW: four

SPEED AT RE-ENTRY TO EARTH'S ATMOSPHERE: 40,200 km/h

TEMPERATURE AT RE-ENTRY: 2,760 °C

Each of Orion's four solar arrays provides enough power to run two small family homes.

Orion had an uncrewed test flight in 2014, soaring to over 5,700 kilometres above Earth before splashing down in the Pacific Ocean.

DID YOU KNOW...?

❓ The launch abort system (LAS) quickly brings the spacecraft back to Earth if there's an emergency during take-off.

❓ The four solar arrays attached to Orion's service module are seven metres long and two metres wide.

❓ The service module has about 20,000 parts that need to be exactly the right size and shape to ensure safe travel.

PERSEVERANCE ROVER

Perseverance will be the most complex and clever robotic rover ever to land on the planet. One of the most exciting things it will do is collect Martian rocks and surface samples in tubes and store them in a special place on Mars. These can then be collected by future missions and studied back on Earth in much greater detail. Perseverance will also carry out an experiment to create oxygen from the Martian atmosphere, which will be vital if astronauts are to stay on the planet for long periods. It will also monitor changes in the weather and the environment.

DIMENSIONS: 3 m long, 2.7 m wide, 2.2 m high

PLANNED LAUNCH: July or August 2020

PLANNED LANDING: February 2021

LAUNCH ROCKET: Two stage Atlas V-541

LAUNCH COST: $243 million

Even with all its gadgets, the Perseverance rover's Earth weight is 1,050 kilograms (that's less than a small car). On Mars, it weighs just 400 kilograms!

DID YOU KNOW...?

❓ Perseverance will take a small helicopter with it. It will need 10 times the power of a normal helicopter to fly in the thin atmosphere.

❓ Curiosity cruises at 0.14 km/h, Perseverance has a top speed of 0.16 km/h, but Opportunity and Spirit are the fastest rovers with a shared top speed of 0.18 km/h.

❓ Perseverance will have 23 cameras in total.

Like Opportunity and Spirit, Perseverance will carry a drill to explore Martian rocks and soil. It will also have at least one microphone to record sounds on Mars for the first time, as well as the sounds made when the rover lands on the surface. Perseverance's SuperCam has the power to capture a tiny dot from over seven metres away. SuperCam also has a laser to vaporise tiny amounts of rock – analysing the colours of the light this produces will help scientists discover what the rock is made from. The mission is set to launch in July or August 2020 when the position of Earth and Mars means the spacecraft will need less power to make the journey. The mission will hopefully last at least 687 Earth days.

THE GAS GIANTS

Get ready for some BIG planetary facts and figures! Jupiter, Saturn, Uranus and Neptune orbit outside of the asteroid belt and they are the biggest planets in the solar system. They are called the gas giants because they don't have a solid surface so you couldn't land a spacecraft on them! Jupiter, the fifth planet from the Sun, is by far the largest. It is 11 times wider than Earth and 1,321 Earths could fit inside it. It is more than twice as heavy as all the other planets put together. Jupiter also has the most satellites – there are 53 moons that are definitely orbiting it and possibly 16 more!

JUPITER
RADIUS*: 69,911 km **ADFS*:** 778 million km

SATURN
RADIUS: 58,232 km **ADFS:** 1.4 billion km

URANUS
RADIUS: 25,362 km **ADFS:** 2.9 billion km

NEPTUNE
RADIUS: 24,622 km **ADFS:** 4.5 billion km

*all radii are averages *average distance from the Sun

*All four of the gas giants are mainly
made up of hydrogen and helium.*

DID YOU KNOW...?

❓ Uranus and Neptune are called the ice giants because their mantles (between the core and the surface) are made of frozen water, methane and ammonia.

❓ Because Neptune is so far from the Sun, the sunshine there is about 900 times dimmer than the sunshine on Earth.

❓ Saturn is the only planet in the solar system that is less dense than water. If it could fit in a giant bathtub, it would float!

Jupiter is home to the biggest storm in the solar system. Called the Great Red Spot, it's twice the size of Earth and it has been raging for over 300 years! Saturn is one of the most spectacular planets. Seen through a telescope, or in images captured by spacecraft such as Cassini, its stunning rings look like magical bands circling the massive ball of gas. It has seven main rings. These rings are the remains of moons, comets and asteroids that were smashed apart by Saturn's incredible gravity, or leftovers from the formation of the solar system. The ice, rock and dust particles range in size from tiny grains to pieces as big as mountains! Each of the rings orbits around Saturn at a different speed.

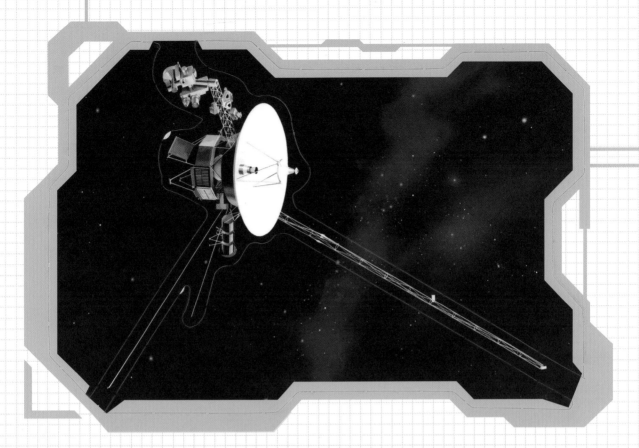

VOYAGER SPACE PROBES

Two of NASA's most incredible spacecraft are the Voyager 1 and 2 probes. At first, NASA planned to use them to study Jupiter and Saturn, but their development prior to launch was so successful that studies of Neptune and Uranus were also included. They launched in 1977 and they are still travelling, making them the most distant human-made objects in space. By 2020, Voyager 1 had travelled over 22 billion kilometres from Earth and Voyager 2 had journeyed more than 18 billion kilometres. Voyager 1 is slightly faster, with an estimated velocity of 61,000 kilometres an hour in relation to the Sun.

LAUNCHED:
20 August 1977 (Voyager 2)
5 September 1977 (Voyager 1)

- - - - - - - - - - - - - - - - - - - -

MASS: 722 kg each

- - - - - - - - - - - - - - - - - - - -

LAUNCH ROCKET: Titan III Centaur

- - - - - - - - - - - - - - - - - - - -

MISSION COST: over $988 million

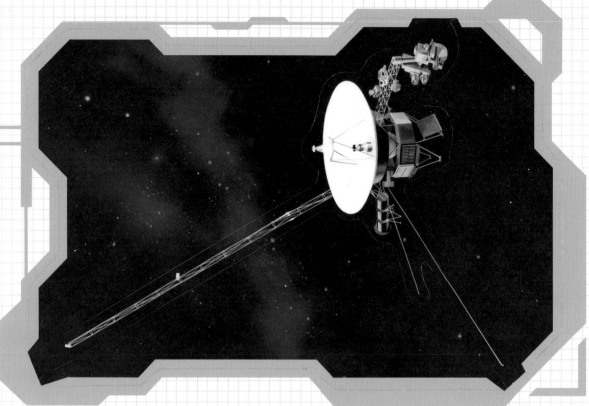

*Both Voyagers were made from
aluminium and alloys.*

DID YOU KNOW...?

❓ The launch date in 1977 took advantage
of a rare arrangement of the outer planets.
This only occurs about every 175 years.

❓ Voyager 1 and 2 are too far from the Sun
to use solar energy. They are powered by
radioactive decay from plutonium.

❓ Radio signals from Voyager 1 take about
17 hours to reach Earth.

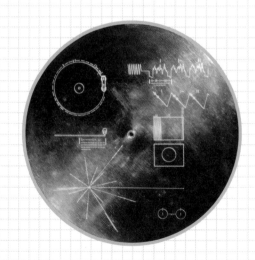

*Voyager 1 and 2 both carry a disc, called the Golden
Record, with images and sounds from Earth to show
extraterrestrial life what our planet is like.*

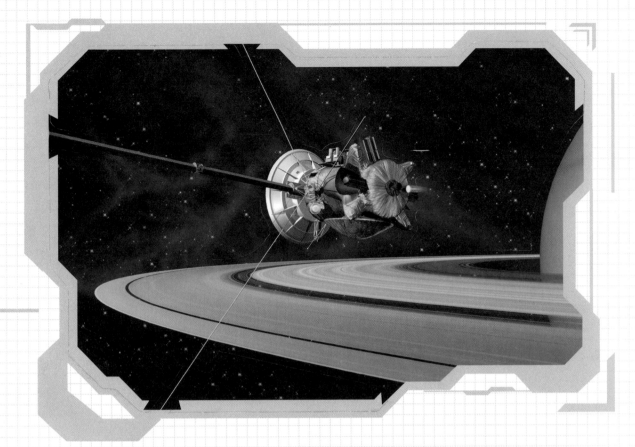

CASSINI-HUYGENS MISSION

Lasting 20 years, this amazing mission has given scientists a much better understanding of Saturn and its many rings and moons. The Cassini spacecraft also achieved flybys of the planets Venus and Jupiter after its launch in October 1997. Cassini's primary role was to release a smaller probe, called Huygens, to land on Saturn's biggest moon, Titan. When this was achieved on 14 January 2005, it became the first human-made machine to touch down on another planet's moon. After it had used up its rocket fuel, scientists crashed Cassini into Saturn's atmosphere on 15 September 2017.

DISTANCE COVERED: 7.8 billion km

- -

FLYBYS OF SATURN'S MOONS: 162

- -

NUMBER OF IMAGES TAKEN: 453,048

- -

NUMBER OF ORBITS OF SATURN: 294

- -

SPEED WHEN SIGNAL LOST IN 2017: 111,637 km/h

The Cassini orbiter carried 12 instruments on board that it used to study Saturn.

The Huygens probe took two hours and 27 minutes to descend to Titan and survived for 72 minutes on the surface.

DID YOU KNOW...?

❓ This mission was named after two famous astronomers: Christiaan Huygens and Jean-Dominique Cassini.

❓ Cassini was the largest interplanetary spacecraft ever built, at 6.7 metres high and four metres wide.

❓ The Cassini-Huygens mission cost a grand total of $3.9 billion. That's an average yearly spend of $195 million!

PLUTO and the DWARF PLANETS

luto formed around 4.5 billion years ago, but it wasn't discovered until 1930. Scientists originally thought of it as the ninth planet from the Sun but in 2006 Pluto was given a new classification: dwarf planet. The gravity of dwarf planets is too low to pull in nearby objects but, like all planets, they do not bump into objects that share their orbit because they move at the same speed. Pluto is about two thirds the width of the Moon and its surface temperature can drop to a freezing -240 °C. In 2015, the New Horizons spacecraft discovered that Pluto has snow-like particles falling in places on its surface.

PLUTO
RADIUS: 1,151 km ADFS: 5.9 billion km

CERES
RADIUS: 476 km ADFS: 413 million km

ERIS
RADIUS: 1,163 km ADFS: 6.2 billion km

MAKEMAKE
RADIUS: 715 km ADFS: 6.8 billion km

HAUMEA
RADIUS: 620 km ADFS: 6.4 billion km

Pluto has five known moons. The largest, Charon,
is about half the size of the dwarf planet it orbits.

DID YOU KNOW...?

❓ Ceres takes 1,682 Earth days to complete its orbit of the Sun – that's more than four and a half years!

❓ Haumea was nicknamed Santa because it was discovered around Christmastime in 2004. Its fast spin makes it look more like a rugby ball, though!

❓ The start of the Kuiper Belt is around 4.4 billion kilometres from the Sun. Experts think there could be over a trillion comets there.

There are four other recognised dwarf planets – Ceres, Eris, Makemake and Haumea. Apart from Ceres, all of the dwarf planets orbit the Sun in a faraway zone beyond Neptune called the Kuiper Belt. Eris is about the same size as Pluto. Makemake is smaller than either Eris or Pluto, and is the brightest object you can spot in the Kuiper Belt. Haumea is one of the speediest large objects rotating in the solar system. Ceres is the largest object in the asteroid belt and is closer to the Sun than Jupiter. It was first spotted over 200 years ago, in 1801, and in 2015 NASA's Dawn spacecraft visited Ceres. This was the first time a dwarf planet had been reached by a human probe.

NEW HORIZONS SPACECRAFT

New Horizons is the perfect name for this deep space mission because it really is showing us new sights! NASA launched it in January 2006. By being the first mission to Pluto, it also became the first mission to explore a Kuiper Belt Object (KBO) and the first to study an ice dwarf planet. In 2015, New Horizons spent six months capturing images of Pluto and its moons, flying just 12,550 kilometres from the planet's surface. In 2018, it set a record by capturing an image while it was 6.12 billion kilometres from Earth – it was of a galactic open star cluster.

LENGTH: 2.1 m

WIDTH: 2.7 m

LAUNCH WEIGHT: 478 kg

DAILY DISTANCE COVERED: 1.1 million km

PROJECT COST: approximately $700 million

New Horizons keeps heat in a bit like a vacuum flask does. Its gold-coloured thermal insulation blankets keep the spacecraft between 10 °C and 30 °C.

DID YOU KNOW...?

❓ The New Horizons cameras have to work in conditions where there is 1,000 times less light than daytime on Earth.

❓ Radio signals took four hours and 25 minutes to travel to Earth during its mission to Pluto.

❓ During its closest approach to Jupiter, New Horizons reached top speeds of more than 75,000 kilometres an hour.

New Horizons has seven main instruments on board, all with special names. Ralph is a camera that takes multicoloured images. Alice is another camera that looks at Pluto's atmosphere and REX is a special instrument that does the same. LORRI is a long-range telescopic camera that maps Pluto's far side. SWAP studies how Pluto interacts with solar wind. PEPSSI studies ions escaping Pluto's atmosphere and SDC measures space dust. New Horizons is designed to use very little power. During its Pluto mission, New Horizons needed less energy than it would take to power two 100-watt light bulbs. It is often put into hibernation for five or six months to reduce costs and wear and tear.

COMETS, METEOROIDS AND METEORS

There are some spectacular sights in space. Comets are speeding balls of frozen gases, rock and dust. They orbit the Sun and are made from materials left over from when the planets formed. The centre of a comet is called the nucleus. As a comet gets nearer to the Sun, the frozen gases around it heat up and expand to create a tail that can stretch for millions of kilometres. When meteroids hit the Earth's atmosphere they become meteors, also known as shooting stars, which burn up and create streaks of light across the sky. Meteoroids that make it through the atmosphere and land on Earth are meteorites.

KNOWN NUMBER OF COMETS IN 2018:
3,052

ESTIMATED METEORITIC MATERIAL REACHING EARTH EVERY DAY: 44,000 kg

LARGE METEORITES FOUND ON EARTH:
over 50,000

METEORITE IMPACT CRATERS FOUND ON EARTH:
around 170

Of the more than 50,000 meteorites that have been found on Earth, 99.8 per cent come from asteroids.

DID YOU KNOW...?

❓ In 2015, the SOHO spacecraft discovered its 3,000th comet. Before its launch in 1995, fewer than 1,000 had been identified.

❓ Because there's no air on the Moon, meteoroids crash into the lunar surface without burning up.

❓ The famous Halley's Comet can only be seen from Earth about every 76 years. It will next be visible in 2061.

The Kuiper Belt is a vast bagel-shaped region of space out beyond Neptune. This mysterious region could be home to trillions of comets as well as many thousands of icy objects measuring more than 100 km across. Some of these objects, including the dwarf planet Pluto, have their own moons. On the outer edges of the Kuiper Belt is the Oort Cloud, which is around 100,000 times further away from the Sun than the Earth is. Comets in the Oort Cloud can take up to 30 million years just to orbit the Sun. Before the New Horizons mission, only the Hubble Space Telescope and powerful telescopes on Earth could see the Kuiper Belt and provide information about the comets and icy bodies there.

ROSETTA SPACE PROBE

One of the European Space Agency's most successful missions involved the long-distance spacecraft Rosetta. In 2014, it became the first machine to land on a comet, after touching down on 67P/Churyumov-Gerasimenko. Rosetta's epic journey to the comet took over 10 years, during which time it made three gravity assist manoeuvres (or speed-increasing swing-bys) of Earth and one of Mars. The mission ended in September 2016 after Rosetta had travelled more than 42 times the distance between the Earth and the Sun and sent back amazing data about the comet and deep space.

DIMENSIONS OF SPACECRAFT, EXCLUDING WINGS:
2.8 m long, 2 m wide

DIMENSIONS OF SOLAR ARRAYS: 32 m wide

LAUNCH WEIGHT:
3,000 kg

MAXIMUM DISTANCE FROM EARTH:
approximately 1 billion km

PROJECT COST:
€1.4 billion

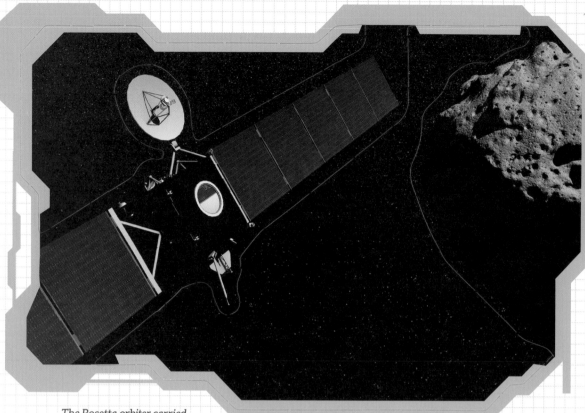

The Rosetta orbiter carried instruments that studied the comet's nucleus (centre) as well as its tail.

DID YOU KNOW...?

❓ The Philae lander was box-shaped and about one metre high and wide. Its mass was 100 kilograms.

❓ When it landed, Philae bounced on the surface of the comet and then continued to fly across it for two more hours.

❓ Philae had instruments that drilled more than 20 centimetres into the comet to study its surface and structure.

A small lander, called Philae, was released from Rosetta and landed on the comet in 2014.

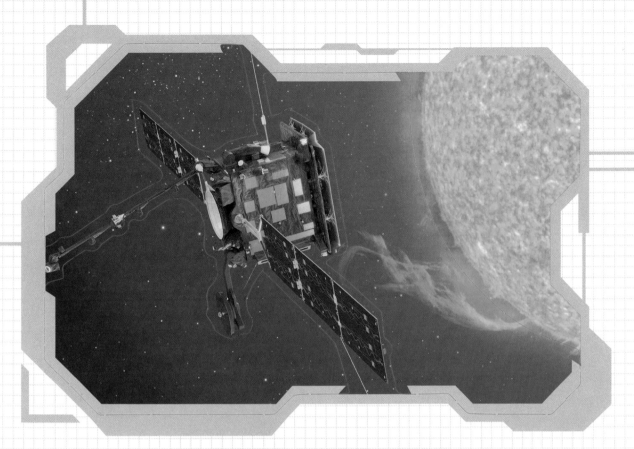

SOLAR ORBITER

launched in February 2020, Solar Orbiter is part of a joint mission between NASA and the ESA. Their shared goal is to get this space satellite closer to the Sun than any other spacecraft before it. The images that Solar Orbiter takes will help scientists understand the Sun and the unmapped inner regions of the solar system much better. At its closest point, Solar Orbiter will be about 42 million kilometres from the Sun – which may sound far away but in fact is even closer to the Sun than Mercury! It will take the satellite around three years to make its epic journey of approximately 108 billion kilometres.

DIMENSIONS, EXCLUDING ARRAYS AND ANTENNAE:
3 m wide, 2.5 m high, 2.5 m deep

- - - - - - - - - - - - - - - - - -

MASS: 1,800 kg

- - - - - - - - - - - - - - - - - -

LAUNCH SITE: Cape Canaveral, Florida, USA

- - - - - - - - - - - - - - - - - -

CLOSEST DISTANCE TO THE SUN: 42 million km

- - - - - - - - - - - - - - - - - -

EXPECTED MISSION DURATION: 7 years

- - - - - - - - - - - - - - - - - -

COST: approximately €850 million

Solar Orbiter will be the first satellite to take close-up images of the Sun's polar regions, which are very difficult to spot from Earth.

DID YOU KNOW...?

❓ Once Solar Orbiter is in position, it will swing close to the Sun every five months, getting nearer than any other spacecraft has got before.

❓ Solar Orbiter will use gravity assist manoeuvres from the planet Venus to help take it further towards the Sun.

❓ In the 1970s, a spacecraft called Helios 2 flew to within 43.432 million kilometres of the Sun.

Because Solar Orbiter will travel nearly three quarters of the way to the Sun, it will be exposed to extremely high temperatures. The sunlight it will face will be 13 times more powerful than the sunlight felt on Earth and the temperature could reach 520 °C – that's a lot hotter than most household ovens! The spacecraft will always be pointed directly at the Sun, so it has a thick heat shield that is larger than the main body of the satellite. The shield's outer layer is made of titanium, which is a very strong, light metal, plus many foil layers that will provide the orbiter's sensitive equipment with maximum protection from the Sun's powerful heat and light rays.

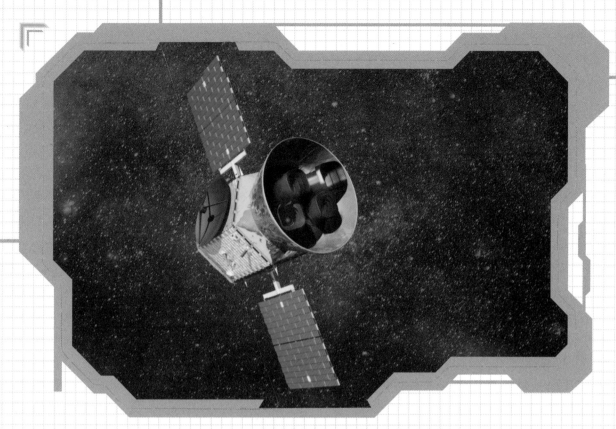

THE TRANSITING EXOPLANET SURVEY SATELLITE

Launched by NASA, the Transiting Exoplanet Survey Satellite (TESS) is a space telescope searching for exoplanets (planets outside our solar system) and possibly finding places where life could exist! TESS's four wide-view cameras will survey over 200,000 of the brightest stars near the Sun. During their mission, they will study 26 different sections of the sky in detail for at least 27 days each in the hunt for clues that planets exist. Scientists expect that TESS will find at least 500 planets that are between the same size and twice the size of Earth.

LAUNCHED: 18 April 2018

DIMENSIONS, INCLUDING ARRAYS:
3.9 m x 1.2 m x 1.5 m

LAUNCH MASS: 325 kg

EXPECTED MISSION DURATION: 2 years

PROJECT COST: $243 million

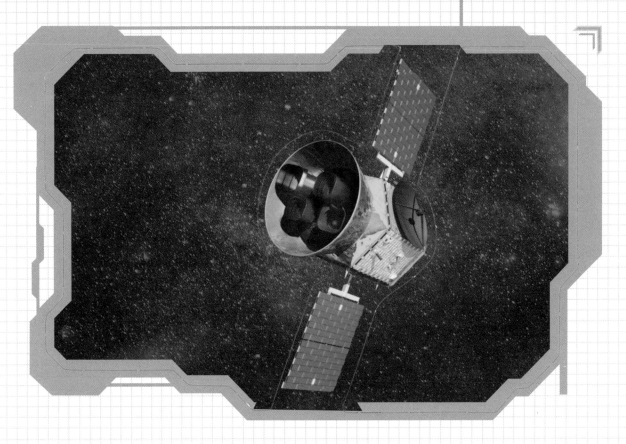

TESS will study the whole sky by breaking it up into 26 different sections.

DID YOU KNOW...?

❓ During its two-year mission, TESS will orbit between 373,400 kilometres and 107,800 kilometres away from Earth.

❓ After it has spent nearly 70 days in space, TESS will start observing the sky. At this stage, one orbit of Earth will take 13.7 days.

❓ Exoplanets that TESS finds will be studied in more depth by telescopes such as the Hubble and the forthcoming James Webb Space Telescopes.

By May 2018, scientists had confirmed that almost 3,000 stars in our galaxy have planets orbiting them. They had also confirmed that almost 4,000 exoplanets had been discovered. Nearly 1,000 of these exoplanets are thought to have a solid, rocky surface like Earth and Mars, which may mean they could support life. One of TESS's jobs will be to spot transits. A transit is the name given to a dip in starlight caused by a planet moving in front of its star. Transits are proof of the existence of planets and nearly 80 per cent of exoplanets have been found by transit-spotting. It is hoped that TESS will help confirm the existence of thousands of exoplanets in the coming years.

THE SPITZER SPACE TELESCOPE

For more than 15 years, the Spitzer Space Telescope has been exploring space and detecting amazing features such as the centres of galaxies and new planetary systems. Spitzer is an infrared telescope, which means it detects heat rather than light. This means it can 'see' into the darkest depths of space and discover much more than optical space telescopes that gather and focus light rather than heat. For the first five and a half years of its mission, Spitzer used liquid helium to keep it at an extremely cool -273 °C. Spitzer has nearly 300,000 infrared detectors to observe objects in deep space.

LAUNCHED: 25 August 2003

- -

LAUNCH MASS: 860 kg

- -

DIAMETER OF TELESCOPE: 85 cm

- -

DISTANCE FROM EARTH:
approximately 250 million km

- -

PROJECT COST: $2.2 billion

The telescope was named after scientist Lyman Spitzer. He first proposed placing a large telescope in space and helped develop Hubble.

DID YOU KNOW…?

❓ The Spitzer Space Telescope had an initial life span of five years, but has performed way beyond that and could stay in operation until at least 2020.

❓ The Spitzer Space Telescope used to be called the Space Infrared Telescope Facility.

❓ Spitzer is the fourth and final part of NASA's Great Observatories program, which also includes the Hubble Space Telescope.

The Spitzer Space Telescope, which is about the same size as a car, follows the Earth as it orbits the Sun. This Earth-following orbit is also known as a heliocentric orbit. As well as keeping it cool, this clever route means that Spitzer's view of the sky is only limited by the Sun. As a result, this amazing telescope has an extremely wide field of vision that allows scientists to observe about a third of the sky at any one time. Many magnificent images have been taken by Spitzer during its time in space, from newly made stars and distant galaxies to stunning supernovas – massive, incredibly bright explosions that occur in the final stages of a star's life.

THE **EXTREMELY LARGE TELESCOPE**

Nicknamed the 'biggest eye on the sky', the Extremely Large Telescope (ELT) is set to become a true space telescope record breaker! Planned for completion in 2024, the ELT will be the biggest telescope of its kind on Earth. It will help to spot planets around other stars – hopefully including some like Earth, supermassive black holes and the first objects that were created in the Universe. The enormous telescope will be housed in a rotating dome that's 89 metres wide and weighs five million kilograms. It has a special design that uses five mirrors, with a huge main mirror made of hundreds of segments.

LOCATION: Atacama Desert, northern Chile

ALTITUDE: 3,046 m above sea level

DIAMETER OF MAIN MIRROR: 39 m

FIRST LIGHT (FIRST USE): 2024

ESTIMATED COST: $1.29 billion

*The European Southern Observatory has been
working on the ELT project since 2005 – it'll take
nearly 20 years for it to finally come alive!*

DID YOU KNOW...?

❓ The ELT will be able to gather 100 million times more light than the human eye.

❓ The ELT is part of the European Southern Observatory's mission to boost our telescopic understanding of the Universe.

❓ The ELT's huge mirror is almost half the length of a football pitch! It consists of 798 pieces that are 1.4 metres wide and five centimetres thick.

Designed in Europe, the ELT is set high up on a mountain called Cerro Armazones, in Chile, South America. In 2014, construction workers began exploding the 5,000 cubic metres of rock that need to be removed to make the top of the mountain level for the telescope. When it is completed, the ELT will be able to capture images that are 16 times sharper than those of the Hubble. It will also be able to take shots of the landing sites on the Moon, although it won't be able to take images of the equipment left behind, such as Moon buggies or Lunar Modules. These objects are too small even for this record-breakingly big telescope to pick up. A ground-based telescope would need to be 200 metres wide to see a Moon buggy!

VOSTOCHNY COSMODROME

ussia, which was once part of the Soviet Union (or USSR), has played a vital role in space travel and exploration. It sent the first object (the Sputnik I satellite) into Earth's orbit in 1957 and the first human (Yuri Gagarin) into space in 1961. Russia is now building Vostochny Cosmodrome in the far east of the country. This spaceport will blast spacecraft into orbit, take cosmonauts and astronauts outside Earth's atmosphere and support deep space exploration. Its first test rocket launch was in 2016. At its widest point, Vostochny Cosmodrome is 36 kilometres across!

LOCATION: Tsiolkovsky, Russia

SIZE: 700 km²

CONSTRUCTION BEGAN: 2011

CONTROLLED BY: Roscosmos

ESTIMATED COST: $7.5 billion

Vostochny Cosmodrome could have
a total area of 700 km² and seven
launch pads when it is completed.

Vostochny's new mobile service tower is
52 metres tall and has seven tiers. This is where
rockets are prepared for launch.

DID YOU KNOW...?

❓ In Russian, 'vostochny' means 'eastern'
and 'cosmodrome' means 'spaceport',
so Vostochny Cosmodrome means
'eastern spaceport'.

❓ Around 170 km of roads and railway
lines will be constructed as part of the new
Vostochny Cosmodrome.

❓ Vostochny is 5,600 kilometres east of
Moscow and Russia's other spaceport,
Baikonur Cosmodrome, is in Kazakhstan.